MW00700899

The Bucket List

Dedicated to Adventurers Everywhere

The Bucket List
Copyright © 2021 Open Book Media, LLC
ISBN: 978-1-954457-03-4
Cover Image courtesy of Free Images, Pixabay
All other images courtesy of Pixabay contributors.
All rights reserved.

This Bucket List belongs to

_____

_____

and covers the dates between
__/__/____ and __/__/____

INTRODUCTION

Welcome to The Bucket List, the book to list your dreams, then make them happen. The Bucket List items are divided into four categories: Adventure, Travel, Skills, and Life and Love. Select from the suggestions offered throughout this book, or use them to create your own ideas. As you accomplish each goal, note your thoughts about your achievement, rate the experience, and include a few photos to remember the moment for all time. (Note: we recommend using self-adhesive photo paper. Do NOT use glue or tape as it will diminish the quality of your book.) Ready to begin living your best life? Let's go!

> Bucket List [Noun] - a number of experiences or achievements that a person hopes to have or accomplish during their lifetime.

CREATE YOUR LIST

When people think of bucket list items, many think of big, over-the-top moments like bungee-jumping or running a marathon, but they don't have to be. Your bucket list can include items as simple as "watch a sunrise on the beach" or "learn to cook Italian" as they can be adventurous. Bucket list items also don't need to be time consuming or involve large amounts of money. Maybe one of your goals is to go to Italy, but for now, you can get a passport and learn Italian. Or maybe you want to own your own business. Start with manageable tasks like creating a business plan and buying your website domain. Only you know what fits your current lifestyle and only you know your true passions. This book is meant to reflect on you, whether as an individual or a couple pursuing common goals.

One final thought about bucket lists. There is room for fifty bucket list items in this book, but you in no way need to list fifty items in one setting. Bucket lists aren't meant to be created or accomplished overnight. They're meant to grow and change, just like you. Start with those items you wish to pursue first then add additional goals and adventures as your life progresses.

Once you make a decision, the universe conspires to make it happen. ~ Ralph Waldo Emerson

WHAT IF I GET STUCK FOR IDEAS ?

If you get stuck, or just want to explore new ideas, ask yourself these questions or check the suggestion lists on the following pages. If you really feel adventurous, flip a coin on one of the pages and see where it lands, then select that idea or a similar one. Pinterest and Instagram are also great sites full of ideas.

- What countries or places have always fascinated you?
- What language have you always wanted to speak?
- What sport have you always longed to play?
- What topic do you wish you knew more about?
- What degree or certification would you like to earn?
- What physically challenging obstacle would you like to conquer?
- What fear would you like to overcome?
- What bad habit would you like to get rid of?
- What subject would you like to be an expert in?
- What could you do to make a real difference in someone's life?
- What act of generosity could you do for a stranger?
- What charitable cause are you passionate about?
- What second, third, or fourth careers would you choose if given the chance?
- What instrument have you always wanted to play?
- What game have you longed to learn?
- What is something you would like to collect?
- What have you always wanted to create from hand?
- What hobby have you always wished to pursue?
- What would your ultimate dream be, if money and time weren't an obstacle?

There are so many options out there to choose from, but pick five or ten per year, large and small, and you'll be well on your way to learning, growing, achieving, and experiencing life to the fullest. At Open Book Media, we just want you to live your best life.

All our dreams can come true, if we have the courage to pursue them ~ Walt Disney

Adventures

Drive a race car	Go zip-lining	Ride in a hot air balloon
Go sky-diving	Sing karaoke	Go scuba-diving
Swim with dolphins	Go whale watching	Pet a shark
Parasail	Cliff-jump	Kayak
Float a lazy river	Go whitewater rafting	Watch sea turtles hatch
Compete in a triathlon	Hike a fourteener	Run a marathon
Ice Skate outdoors at Christmas	Admire the view at the top of the Empire State Building	Do a ride-along with a police officer
Dine at a 5-star restaurant	Ride a horse on the beach	Bungee jump off a bridge
Go windsurfing	Sail the Caribbean	Go Jet Skiing
Stand on all seven continents	Be in two places at the same time	Stand at the top of Pike's Peak
Mountain bike in Utah	Camp under the stars	Attend a Broadway show
Be an extra in a movie	Skinny-Dip in a Lake	Fly-fish in the Rockies
Take a Ferrari for a test drive	Drive the Pacific coast highway	Be a contestant on a game show

A comfort zone is a beautiful place, but nothing ever grows there. ~ Anonymous

Travel

Cruise the Caribbean	Backpack across Europe	Drive Route 66
Attend carnival in Rio de Janeiro	Participate in Día de los Muertos in Mexico City	Run with the bulls in Pamplona, Spain
See the Dead Sea	Take a Biblical tour in Israel	Visit the Wailing Wall
Eat gelato in Florence	Drive the Amalfi coast	Ride a gondola in Venice
Visit the Grand Canyon	Marvel at Mount Rushmore	Visit all 50 states
Ride the Chunnel from London to Paris	Stay at the Ice Hotel in Sweden	Tour the Holocaust museum in Amsterdam
Tour the Louvre in Paris	Go on an African Safari	Marvel Easter Island
Walk the Great Wall of China	Go birdwatching in Costa Rica	Climb the stairs in Machu Picchu, Peru
Tour the White House	Go wine-tasting in California	Visit the Smithsonian
Watch the changing of the guard in London	Take a polar plunge in Antarctica	Dive the Great Barrier Reef in Australia
Ride a train across the U.S.	Visit the castles of Ireland	Hike the Appalachian Trail
Drive the Blue Ridge Parkway in autumn	Marvel the Aurora Borealis In Alaska	Camp in Yellowstone National Park .

I am not the same, having seen the moon shine on the other side of the world. ~ Mary Anne Rademacher

Skills

Learn to ballroom dance	Memorize all the Presidents of the U.S. in order	Take a cooking class
Practice yoga or Tai-Chi	Become a wine connoisseur	Learn a foreign language
Make your own beer	Learn to play an instrument	Make your own wine
Take up pottery	Master origami	Learn to paint
Read 100 classic novels	Take up photography	Master public speaking
Study Greek mythology	Study Renaissance art	Study Roman history
Earn a Master's degree	Become a Notary Public	Collect stamps or coins
Become a certified Minister and conduct a wedding	Get your black-belt in a martial arts discipline	Read and study the Bible cover to cover
Learn to play chess	Learn to ride a motorcycle	Learn to shoot a gun
Become a master poker player	Study sign language	Become the next Jeopardy champion
Get your pilot's license	Earn a law degree	Write poetry
Learn songwriting	Get a Bachelor's degree	Learn calligraphy
Write and publish a book	Try a new sport	Become an interior designer

Live as if you were to die tomorrow. Learn as if you were to live forever. ~ Mahatma Gandhi

Life and Love

Get married	Have a child	Adopt a child
Coach your kids' team	Watch your kids' first steps	Attend your kids' weddings
Start your own business	Make a million dollars	Land your dream job
Help a homeless person	Buy someone's groceries	Pay off someone's debt
Send a message in a bottle	Go on a blind date	Invite a stranger to dinner
Visit the residents at a nursing home	Celebrate with an expensive bottle of champagne	Write and record your own love song
Throw someone a surprise party	Attend the church services of five different religions	Host a foreign exchange student
Reconnect with a lost friend	Forgive someone	Break a bad habit
Create a time capsule and open it 25 years later	Experience your fifteen minutes of fame	Teach someone how to read
Volunteer for a charity	Create a movement	Raise money for a cause
Start a non-profit	Join the military	Minister the lost
Plant a tree, or several	Become someone's mentor	Join the Peace Corp
Adopt or foster an animal	Research your ancestry	Say I love you daily

Have a heart that never hardens, a temper that never tires, and a touch that never hurts.~ Charles Dickens

Bucket List Item	Category	Date Achieved
1.		☐
2.		☐
3.		☐
4.		☐
5.		☐
6.		☐
7.		☐
8.		☐
9.		☐
10.		☐
11.		☐
12.		☐
13.		☐
14.		☐
15.		☐
16.		☐
17.		☐
18.		☐
19.		☐
20.		☐
21.		☐
22.		☐
23.		☐
24.		☐
25.		☐

Bucket List Item	Category	Date Achieved
26.		☐
27.		☐
28.		☐
29.		☐
30.		☐
31.		☐
32.		☐
33.		☐
34.		☐
35.		☐
36.		☐
37.		☐
38.		☐
39.		☐
40.		☐
41.		☐
42.		☐
43.		☐
44.		☐
45.		☐
46.		☐
47.		☐
48.		☐
49.		☐
50.		☐

Bucket List Item: _____ #____

Date: _____ **Where:** _____

Others Present: _____

The Proof

Insert 3x5 Photo

The Moment

_____

_____

_____

_____

_____

_____

_____

_____

_____

_____

_____

_____

_____

_____

The Facts

Why was achieving this item important to you? _____

_____

_____

What obstacles did you have to overcome to accomplish this item?

_____

_____

_____

How did your success make you feel? _____

_____

_____

RATE IT

❑ 5 Stars: Changed my life
❑ 4 Stars: Amazing
❑ 3 Stars: I'd do it again
❑ 2 Stars: Once was enough
❑ 1 Star : Not what I expected

Insert 2x2 Photo

Insert 3x5 Photo

Bucket List Item: _____ #____

Date: _____ **Where:** _____

Others Present: _____

The Proof

Insert 3x5 Photo

The Moment

_____
_____
_____
_____
_____
_____
_____
_____
_____
_____
_____
_____
_____

The Facts

Why was achieving this item important to you? _____

_____

_____

What obstacles did you have to overcome to accomplish this item?

_____

_____

_____

How did your success make you feel? _____

_____

_____

RATE IT
❑ 5 Stars: Changed my life
❑ 4 Stars: Amazing
❑ 3 Stars: I'd do it again
❑ 2 Stars: Once was enough
❑ 1 Star : Not what I expected

Insert 2x2 Photo

Insert 3x5 Photo

Bucket List Item: _____ #_____

Date: _____ **Where:** _____

Others Present: _____

The Proof

Insert 3x5 Photo

The Moment

_____
_____
_____
_____
_____
_____
_____
_____
_____
_____
_____
_____
_____
_____

The Facts

Why was achieving this item important to you? _____
_____
_____

What obstacles did you have to overcome to accomplish this item?
_____
_____
_____

How did your success make you feel? _____
_____
_____

RATE IT

❑ 5 Stars: Changed my life
❑ 4 Stars: Amazing
❑ 3 Stars: I'd do it again
❑ 2 Stars: Once was enough
❑ 1 Star : Not what I expected

Insert 2x2 Photo

Insert 3x5 Photo

Bucket List Item: _____ #____

Date: _____ **Where:** _____

Others Present: _____

The Proof

Insert 3x5 Photo

The Moment

_____
_____
_____
_____
_____
_____
_____
_____
_____
_____
_____
_____
_____
_____

The Facts

Why was achieving this item important to you? _____

_____

_____

What obstacles did you have to overcome to accomplish this item?

_____

_____

_____

How did your success make you feel? _____

_____

_____

RATE IT

❏ 5 Stars: Changed my life
❏ 4 Stars: Amazing
❏ 3 Stars: I'd do it again
❏ 2 Stars: Once was enough
❏ 1 Star : Not what I expected

Insert 2x2 Photo

Insert 3x5 Photo

Bucket List Item: _____ #_____

Date: _____ **Where:** _____

Others Present: _____

The Proof

Insert 3x5 Photo

The Moment

_____
_____
_____
_____
_____
_____
_____
_____
_____
_____
_____
_____
_____
_____

Why was achieving this item important to you? _____

_____

_____

What obstacles did you have to overcome to accomplish this item?

_____

_____

_____

How did your success make you feel? _____

_____

_____

RATE IT

❑ 5 Stars: Changed my life
❑ 4 Stars: Amazing
❑ 3 Stars: I'd do it again
❑ 2 Stars: Once was enough
❑ 1 Star : Not what I expected

Insert 2x2 Photo

Insert 3x5 Photo

Bucket List Item: _____ #____

Date: _____ **Where:** _____

Others Present: _____

The Proof

Insert 3x5 Photo

The Moment

_____
_____
_____
_____
_____
_____
_____
_____
_____
_____
_____
_____
_____
_____
_____

The Facts

Why was achieving this item important to you? _____

_____

_____

What obstacles did you have to overcome to accomplish this item?

_____

_____

_____

How did your success make you feel? _____

_____

_____

RATE IT

❑ 5 Stars: Changed my life
❑ 4 Stars: Amazing
❑ 3 Stars: I'd do it again
❑ 2 Stars: Once was enough
❑ 1 Star : Not what I expected

Insert 2x2 Photo

Insert 3x5 Photo

Bucket List Item: _____ #_____

Date: _____   **Where:** _____

Others Present: _____

The Proof

Insert 3x5 Photo

The Moment

_____
_____
_____
_____
_____
_____
_____
_____
_____
_____
_____
_____
_____
_____

The Facts

Why was achieving this item important to you? _____

_____

_____

What obstacles did you have to overcome to accomplish this item?

_____

_____

_____

How did your success make you feel? _____

_____

_____

RATE IT

❑ 5 Stars: Changed my life
❑ 4 Stars: Amazing
❑ 3 Stars: I'd do it again
❑ 2 Stars: Once was enough
❑ 1 Star : Not what I expected

Insert 2x2 Photo

Insert 3x5 Photo

Bucket List Item: _____ #____

Date: _____   **Where:** _____

Others Present: _____

The Proof

Insert 3x5 Photo

The Moment

_____
_____
_____
_____
_____
_____
_____
_____
_____
_____
_____
_____
_____
_____

The Facts

Why was achieving this item important to you? _____

_____

_____

What obstacles did you have to overcome to accomplish this item?

_____

_____

_____

How did your success make you feel? _____

_____

_____

RATE IT

❏ 5 Stars: Changed my life
❏ 4 Stars: Amazing
❏ 3 Stars: I'd do it again
❏ 2 Stars: Once was enough
❏ 1 Star : Not what I expected

Insert 2x2 Photo

Insert 3x5 Photo

Bucket List Item: _____ #_____

Date: _____ **Where:** _____

Others Present: _____

Insert 3x5 Photo

The Moment

_____
_____
_____
_____
_____
_____
_____
_____
_____
_____
_____
_____
_____

The Facts

Why was achieving this item important to you? _____

_____

_____

What obstacles did you have to overcome to accomplish this item?

_____

_____

_____

How did your success make you feel? _____

_____

_____

RATE IT

❑ 5 Stars: Changed my life
❑ 4 Stars: Amazing
❑ 3 Stars: I'd do it again
❑ 2 Stars: Once was enough
❑ 1 Star : Not what I expected

Insert 2x2 Photo

Insert 3x5 Photo

Bucket List Item: _____ #____

Date: _____ **Where:** _____

Others Present: _____

Insert 3x5 Photo

The Moment

_____
_____
_____
_____
_____
_____
_____
_____
_____
_____
_____
_____
_____
_____

The Facts

Why was achieving this item important to you? _____
_____
_____

What obstacles did you have to overcome to accomplish this item?
_____
_____
_____

How did your success make you feel? _____
_____
_____

RATE IT

❑ 5 Stars: Changed my life
❑ 4 Stars: Amazing
❑ 3 Stars: I'd do it again
❑ 2 Stars: Once was enough
❑ 1 Star : Not what I expected

Insert 2x2 Photo

Insert 3x5 Photo

Bucket List Item: _____ #_____

Date: _____ **Where:** _____

Others Present: _____

The Proof

Insert 3x5 Photo

The Moment

_____
_____
_____
_____
_____
_____
_____
_____
_____
_____
_____
_____
_____
_____

The Facts

Why was achieving this item important to you? _____

_____

_____

What obstacles did you have to overcome to accomplish this item?

_____

_____

_____

How did your success make you feel? _____

_____

_____

RATE IT

❏ 5 Stars: Changed my life
❏ 4 Stars: Amazing
❏ 3 Stars: I'd do it again
❏ 2 Stars: Once was enough
❏ 1 Star : Not what I expected

Insert 2x2 Photo

Insert 3x5 Photo

Bucket List Item: _____ #_____

Date: _____   **Where:** _____

Others Present: _____

The Proof

Insert 3x5 Photo

The Moment

_____
_____
_____
_____
_____
_____
_____
_____
_____
_____
_____
_____
_____
_____

The Facts

Why was achieving this item important to you? _____

_____

_____

What obstacles did you have to overcome to accomplish this item?

_____

_____

_____

How did your success make you feel? _____

_____

_____

RATE IT

❑ 5 Stars: Changed my life
❑ 4 Stars: Amazing
❑ 3 Stars: I'd do it again
❑ 2 Stars: Once was enough
❑ 1 Star : Not what I expected

Insert 2x2 Photo

Insert 3x5 Photo

Bucket List Item: _____ #____

Date: _____ **Where:** _____

Others Present: _____

The Proof

Insert 3x5 Photo

The Moment

_____
_____
_____
_____
_____
_____
_____
_____
_____
_____
_____
_____
_____
_____

The Facts

Why was achieving this item important to you? _____

_____

_____

What obstacles did you have to overcome to accomplish this item?

_____

_____

_____

How did your success make you feel? _____

_____

_____

RATE IT

- ❏ 5 Stars: Changed my life
- ❏ 4 Stars: Amazing
- ❏ 3 Stars: I'd do it again
- ❏ 2 Stars: Once was enough
- ❏ 1 Star : Not what I expected

Insert 2x2 Photo

Insert 3x5 Photo

Bucket List Item: _____ #____

Date: _____ **Where:** _____

Others Present: _____

The Proof

Insert 3x5 Photo

The Moment

_____
_____
_____
_____
_____
_____
_____
_____
_____
_____
_____
_____
_____
_____

The Facts

Why was achieving this item important to you? _____
_____
_____

What obstacles did you have to overcome to accomplish this item?
_____
_____
_____

How did your success make you feel? _____
_____
_____

RATE IT

❑ 5 Stars: Changed my life
❑ 4 Stars: Amazing
❑ 3 Stars: I'd do it again
❑ 2 Stars: Once was enough
❑ 1 Star : Not what I expected

Insert 2x2 Photo

Insert 3x5 Photo

Bucket List Item: _____ #____

Date: _____ **Where:** _____

Others Present: _____

Insert 3x5 Photo

The Moment

_____
_____
_____
_____
_____
_____
_____
_____
_____
_____
_____
_____
_____
_____

The Facts

Why was achieving this item important to you? _____
_____
_____

What obstacles did you have to overcome to accomplish this item?
_____
_____
_____

How did your success make you feel? _____
_____
_____

RATE IT

- ❑ 5 Stars: Changed my life
- ❑ 4 Stars: Amazing
- ❑ 3 Stars: I'd do it again
- ❑ 2 Stars: Once was enough
- ❑ 1 Star : Not what I expected

Insert 2x2 Photo

Insert 3x5 Photo

Bucket List Item: _____ #_____

Date: _____ **Where:** _____

Others Present: _____

The Proof

Insert 3x5 Photo

The Moment

_____
_____
_____
_____
_____
_____
_____
_____
_____
_____
_____
_____
_____
_____

The Facts

Why was achieving this item important to you? _____

_____

_____

What obstacles did you have to overcome to accomplish this item?

_____

_____

_____

How did your success make you feel? _____

_____

_____

RATE IT

❑ 5 Stars: Changed my life
❑ 4 Stars: Amazing
❑ 3 Stars: I'd do it again
❑ 2 Stars: Once was enough
❑ 1 Star : Not what I expected

Insert 2x2 Photo

Insert 3x5 Photo

Bucket List Item: _____ #_____

Date: _____ **Where:** _____

Others Present: _____

The Proof

Insert 3x5 Photo

The Moment

_____

_____

_____

_____

_____

_____

_____

_____

_____

_____

_____

_____

_____

The Facts

Why was achieving this item important to you? _____
_____
_____

What obstacles did you have to overcome to accomplish this item?
_____
_____
_____

How did your success make you feel? _____
_____
_____

RATE IT

❑ 5 Stars: Changed my life
❑ 4 Stars: Amazing
❑ 3 Stars: I'd do it again
❑ 2 Stars: Once was enough
❑ 1 Star : Not what I expected

Insert 2x2 Photo

Insert 3x5 Photo

Bucket List Item: _____ #____

Date: _____ **Where:** _____

Others Present: _____

The Proof

Insert 3x5 Photo

The Moment

_____
_____
_____
_____
_____
_____
_____
_____
_____
_____
_____
_____
_____
_____

The Facts

Why was achieving this item important to you? _____

_____

_____

What obstacles did you have to overcome to accomplish this item?

_____

_____

_____

How did your success make you feel? _____

_____

_____

RATE IT

❑ 5 Stars: Changed my life
❑ 4 Stars: Amazing
❑ 3 Stars: I'd do it again
❑ 2 Stars: Once was enough
❑ 1 Star : Not what I expected

Insert 2x2 Photo

Insert 3x5 Photo

Bucket List Item: _____ #_____

Date: _____   **Where:** _____

Others Present: _____

The Proof

Insert 3x5 Photo

The Moment

_____
_____
_____
_____
_____
_____
_____
_____
_____
_____
_____
_____
_____

The Facts

Why was achieving this item important to you? _____

_____

_____

What obstacles did you have to overcome to accomplish this item?

_____

_____

_____

How did your success make you feel? _____

_____

_____

RATE IT

❑ 5 Stars: Changed my life
❑ 4 Stars: Amazing
❑ 3 Stars: I'd do it again
❑ 2 Stars: Once was enough
❑ 1 Star : Not what I expected

Insert 2x2 Photo

Insert 3x5 Photo

Bucket List Item: _____ #_____

Date: _____   **Where:** _____

Others Present: _____

The Proof

Insert 3x5 Photo

The Moment

_____
_____
_____
_____
_____
_____
_____
_____
_____
_____
_____
_____
_____
_____
_____
_____

The Facts

Why was achieving this item important to you? _____

_____

_____

What obstacles did you have to overcome to accomplish this item?

_____

_____

_____

How did your success make you feel? _____

_____

_____

RATE IT

❑ 5 Stars: Changed my life
❑ 4 Stars: Amazing
❑ 3 Stars: I'd do it again
❑ 2 Stars: Once was enough
❑ 1 Star : Not what I expected

Insert 2x2 Photo

Insert 3x5 Photo

Bucket List Item: _____ #_____

Date: _____   **Where:** _____

Others Present: _____

The Proof

Insert 3x5 Photo

The Moment

_____
_____
_____
_____
_____
_____
_____
_____
_____
_____
_____
_____
_____
_____
_____

The Facts

Why was achieving this item important to you? _____

_____

_____

What obstacles did you have to overcome to accomplish this item?

_____

_____

_____

How did your success make you feel? _____

_____

_____

RATE IT

❑ 5 Stars: Changed my life
❑ 4 Stars: Amazing
❑ 3 Stars: I'd do it again
❑ 2 Stars: Once was enough
❑ 1 Star : Not what I expected

Insert 2x2 Photo

Insert 3x5 Photo

Bucket List Item: _____ #____

Date: _____ **Where:** _____

Others Present: _____

The Proof

Insert 3x5 Photo

The Moment

_____
_____
_____
_____
_____
_____
_____
_____
_____
_____
_____
_____
_____

The Facts

Why was achieving this item important to you? _____
_____
_____

What obstacles did you have to overcome to accomplish this item?
_____
_____
_____

How did your success make you feel? _____
_____
_____

RATE IT

❏ 5 Stars: Changed my life
❏ 4 Stars: Amazing
❏ 3 Stars: I'd do it again
❏ 2 Stars: Once was enough
❏ 1 Star : Not what I expected

Insert 2x2 Photo

Insert 3x5 Photo

Bucket List Item: _____ #____

Date: _____ **Where:** _____

Others Present: _____

The Proof

Insert 3x5 Photo

The Moment

_____
_____
_____
_____
_____
_____
_____
_____
_____
_____
_____
_____
_____

The Facts

Why was achieving this item important to you? _____

_____

_____

What obstacles did you have to overcome to accomplish this item?

_____

_____

_____

How did your success make you feel? _____

_____

_____

RATE IT

❑ 5 Stars: Changed my life
❑ 4 Stars: Amazing
❑ 3 Stars: I'd do it again
❑ 2 Stars: Once was enough
❑ 1 Star : Not what I expected

Insert 2x2 Photo

Insert 3x5 Photo

Bucket List Item: _____ #____

Date: _____ **Where:** _____

Others Present: _____

The Proof

Insert 3x5 Photo

The Moment

_____

_____

_____

_____

_____

_____

_____

_____

_____

_____

_____

_____

_____

The Facts

Why was achieving this item important to you? _____

_____

_____

What obstacles did you have to overcome to accomplish this item?

_____

_____

_____

How did your success make you feel? _____

_____

_____

RATE IT

❑ 5 Stars: Changed my life
❑ 4 Stars: Amazing
❑ 3 Stars: I'd do it again
❑ 2 Stars: Once was enough
❑ 1 Star : Not what I expected

Insert 2x2 Photo

Insert 3x5 Photo

Bucket List Item: _____ #_____

Date: _____ **Where:** _____

Others Present: _____

The Proof

Insert 3x5 Photo

The Moment

_____
_____
_____
_____
_____
_____
_____
_____
_____
_____
_____
_____
_____
_____

The Facts

Why was achieving this item important to you? _____

_____

_____

What obstacles did you have to overcome to accomplish this item?

_____

_____

_____

How did your success make you feel? _____

_____

_____

RATE IT

- ❑ 5 Stars: Changed my life
- ❑ 4 Stars: Amazing
- ❑ 3 Stars: I'd do it again
- ❑ 2 Stars: Once was enough
- ❑ 1 Star : Not what I expected

Insert 2x2 Photo

Insert 3x5 Photo

Bucket List Item: _____ #_____

Date: _____ **Where:** _____

Others Present: _____

The Proof

Insert 3x5 Photo

The Moment

_____
_____
_____
_____
_____
_____
_____
_____
_____
_____
_____
_____
_____
_____

The Facts

Why was achieving this item important to you? _____

_____

_____

What obstacles did you have to overcome to accomplish this item?

_____

_____

_____

How did your success make you feel? _____

_____

_____

RATE IT

❏ 5 Stars: Changed my life
❏ 4 Stars: Amazing
❏ 3 Stars: I'd do it again
❏ 2 Stars: Once was enough
❏ 1 Star : Not what I expected

Insert 2x2 Photo

Insert 3x5 Photo

Bucket List Item: _____ #____

Date: _____ **Where:** _____

Others Present: _____

The Proof

Insert 3x5 Photo

The Moment

_____
_____
_____
_____
_____
_____
_____
_____
_____
_____
_____
_____
_____

The Facts

Why was achieving this item important to you? _____

_____

_____

What obstacles did you have to overcome to accomplish this item?

_____

_____

_____

How did your success make you feel? _____

_____

_____

RATE IT

❑ 5 Stars: Changed my life
❑ 4 Stars: Amazing
❑ 3 Stars: I'd do it again
❑ 2 Stars: Once was enough
❑ 1 Star : Not what I expected

Insert 2x2 Photo

Insert 3x5 Photo

Bucket List Item: _____ #____

Date: _____ **Where:** _____

Others Present: _____

The Proof

Insert 3x5 Photo

The Moment

_____
_____
_____
_____
_____
_____
_____
_____
_____
_____
_____
_____
_____

The Facts

Why was achieving this item important to you? _____

_____

_____

What obstacles did you have to overcome to accomplish this item?

_____

_____

_____

How did your success make you feel? _____

_____

_____

RATE IT

❑ 5 Stars: Changed my life
❑ 4 Stars: Amazing
❑ 3 Stars: I'd do it again
❑ 2 Stars: Once was enough
❑ 1 Star : Not what I expected

Insert 2x2 Photo

Insert 3x5 Photo

Bucket List Item: _____ #_____

Date: _____ **Where:** _____

Others Present: _____

The Proof

Insert 3x5 Photo

The Moment

_____
_____
_____
_____
_____
_____
_____
_____
_____
_____
_____
_____
_____
_____

The Facts

Why was achieving this item important to you? _____

_____

_____

What obstacles did you have to overcome to accomplish this item?

_____

_____

_____

How did your success make you feel? _____

_____

_____

RATE IT

❑ 5 Stars: Changed my life
❑ 4 Stars: Amazing
❑ 3 Stars: I'd do it again
❑ 2 Stars: Once was enough
❑ 1 Star : Not what I expected

Insert 2x2 Photo

Insert 3x5 Photo

Bucket List Item: _____ #_____

Date: _____ **Where:** _____

Others Present: _____

The Proof

Insert 3x5 Photo

The Moment

_____
_____
_____
_____
_____
_____
_____
_____
_____
_____
_____
_____
_____
_____

The Facts

Why was achieving this item important to you? _____

_____

_____

What obstacles did you have to overcome to accomplish this item?

_____

_____

_____

How did your success make you feel? _____

_____

_____

RATE IT

❑ 5 Stars: Changed my life
❑ 4 Stars: Amazing
❑ 3 Stars: I'd do it again
❑ 2 Stars: Once was enough
❑ 1 Star : Not what I expected

Insert 2x2 Photo

Insert 3x5 Photo

Bucket List Item: _____ #____

Date: _____ **Where:** _____

Others Present: _____

The Proof

Insert 3x5 Photo

The Moment

_____
_____
_____
_____
_____
_____
_____
_____
_____
_____
_____
_____
_____
_____
_____

The Facts

Why was achieving this item important to you? _____
_____
_____

What obstacles did you have to overcome to accomplish this item?
_____
_____
_____

How did your success make you feel? _____
_____
_____

RATE IT

❑ 5 Stars: Changed my life
❑ 4 Stars: Amazing
❑ 3 Stars: I'd do it again
❑ 2 Stars: Once was enough
❑ 1 Star : Not what I expected

Insert 2x2 Photo

Insert 3x5 Photo

Bucket List Item: _____ #_____

Date: _____ **Where:** _____

Others Present: _____

The Proof

Insert 3x5 Photo

The Moment

_____
_____
_____
_____
_____
_____
_____
_____
_____
_____
_____
_____
_____

The Facts

Why was achieving this item important to you? _____
_____
_____

What obstacles did you have to overcome to accomplish this item?
_____
_____
_____

How did your success make you feel? _____
_____
_____

RATE IT

❑ 5 Stars: Changed my life
❑ 4 Stars: Amazing
❑ 3 Stars: I'd do it again
❑ 2 Stars: Once was enough
❑ 1 Star : Not what I expected

Insert 2x2 Photo

Insert 3x5 Photo

Bucket List Item: _____ #_____

Date: _____ **Where:** _____

Others Present: _____

Insert 3x5 Photo

The Moment

_____
_____
_____
_____
_____
_____
_____
_____
_____
_____
_____
_____
_____
_____

The Facts

Why was achieving this item important to you? _____

_____

_____

What obstacles did you have to overcome to accomplish this item?

_____

_____

_____

How did your success make you feel? _____

_____

_____

RATE IT

❑ 5 Stars: Changed my life
❑ 4 Stars: Amazing
❑ 3 Stars: I'd do it again
❑ 2 Stars: Once was enough
❑ 1 Star : Not what I expected

Insert 2x2 Photo

Insert 3x5 Photo

Bucket List Item: _____ #____

Date: _____ **Where:** _____

Others Present: _____

The Proof

Insert 3x5 Photo

The Moment

_____
_____
_____
_____
_____
_____
_____
_____
_____
_____
_____
_____
_____

The Facts

Why was achieving this item important to you? _____

_____

_____

What obstacles did you have to overcome to accomplish this item?

_____

_____

_____

How did your success make you feel? _____

_____

_____

RATE IT

❑ 5 Stars: Changed my life
❑ 4 Stars: Amazing
❑ 3 Stars: I'd do it again
❑ 2 Stars: Once was enough
❑ 1 Star : Not what I expected

Insert 2x2 Photo

Insert 3x5 Photo

Bucket List Item: _____ #____

Date: _____ **Where:** _____

Others Present: _____

The Proof

Insert 3x5 Photo

The Moment

_____
_____
_____
_____
_____
_____
_____
_____
_____
_____
_____
_____
_____
_____

The Facts

Why was achieving this item important to you? _____

_____

_____

What obstacles did you have to overcome to accomplish this item?

_____

_____

_____

How did your success make you feel? _____

_____

_____

RATE IT

❑ 5 Stars: Changed my life
❑ 4 Stars: Amazing
❑ 3 Stars: I'd do it again
❑ 2 Stars: Once was enough
❑ 1 Star : Not what I expected

Insert 2x2 Photo

Insert 3x5 Photo

Bucket List Item: _____ #____

Date: _____ **Where:** _____

Others Present: _____

The Proof

Insert 3x5 Photo

The Moment

_____
_____
_____
_____
_____
_____
_____
_____
_____
_____
_____
_____
_____
_____

The Facts

Why was achieving this item important to you? _____

_____

_____

What obstacles did you have to overcome to accomplish this item?

_____

_____

_____

How did your success make you feel? _____

_____

_____

RATE IT

❑ 5 Stars: Changed my life
❑ 4 Stars: Amazing
❑ 3 Stars: I'd do it again
❑ 2 Stars: Once was enough
❑ 1 Star : Not what I expected

Insert 2x2 Photo

Insert 3x5 Photo

Bucket List Item: _____ #_____

Date: _____ **Where:** _____

Others Present: _____

The Proof

Insert 3x5 Photo

The Moment

_____
_____
_____
_____
_____
_____
_____
_____
_____
_____
_____
_____
_____
_____

The Facts

Why was achieving this item important to you? _____

_____

_____

What obstacles did you have to overcome to accomplish this item?

_____

_____

_____

How did your success make you feel? _____

_____

_____

RATE IT

❑ 5 Stars: Changed my life
❑ 4 Stars: Amazing
❑ 3 Stars: I'd do it again
❑ 2 Stars: Once was enough
❑ 1 Star : Not what I expected

Insert 2x2 Photo

Insert 3x5 Photo

Bucket List Item: _____ #____

Date: _____ **Where:** _____

Others Present: _____

The Proof

Insert 3x5 Photo

The Moment

_____
_____
_____
_____
_____
_____
_____
_____
_____
_____
_____
_____
_____
_____
_____

Why was achieving this item important to you? _____

_____

_____

What obstacles did you have to overcome to accomplish this item?

_____

_____

_____

How did your success make you feel? _____

_____

_____

RATE IT

❑ 5 Stars: Changed my life
❑ 4 Stars: Amazing
❑ 3 Stars: I'd do it again
❑ 2 Stars: Once was enough
❑ 1 Star : Not what I expected

Insert 2x2 Photo

Insert 3x5 Photo

Bucket List Item: _____ #_____

Date: _____ **Where:** _____

Others Present: _____

Insert 3x5 Photo

The Moment

_____
_____
_____
_____
_____
_____
_____
_____
_____
_____
_____
_____
_____
_____

The Facts

Why was achieving this item important to you? _____
_____
_____

What obstacles did you have to overcome to accomplish this item?
_____
_____
_____

How did your success make you feel? _____
_____
_____

RATE IT
❑ 5 Stars: Changed my life
❑ 4 Stars: Amazing
❑ 3 Stars: I'd do it again
❑ 2 Stars: Once was enough
❑ 1 Star : Not what I expected

Insert 2x2 Photo

Insert 3x5 Photo

Bucket List Item: _____ #_____

Date: _____ **Where:** _____

Others Present: _____

The Proof

Insert 3x5 Photo

The Moment

_____
_____
_____
_____
_____
_____
_____
_____
_____
_____
_____
_____
_____

The Facts

Why was achieving this item important to you? _____

_____

_____

What obstacles did you have to overcome to accomplish this item?

_____

_____

_____

How did your success make you feel? _____

_____

_____

RATE IT

❑ 5 Stars: Changed my life
❑ 4 Stars: Amazing
❑ 3 Stars: I'd do it again
❑ 2 Stars: Once was enough
❑ 1 Star : Not what I expected

Insert 2x2 Photo

Insert 3x5 Photo

Bucket List Item: _____ #____

Date: _____ **Where:** _____

Others Present: _____

The Proof

Insert 3x5 Photo

The Moment

_____
_____
_____
_____
_____
_____
_____
_____
_____
_____
_____
_____
_____
_____

The Facts

Why was achieving this item important to you? _____

_____

_____

What obstacles did you have to overcome to accomplish this item?

_____

_____

_____

How did your success make you feel? _____

_____

_____

RATE IT

❑ 5 Stars: Changed my life
❑ 4 Stars: Amazing
❑ 3 Stars: I'd do it again
❑ 2 Stars: Once was enough
❑ 1 Star : Not what I expected

Insert 2x2 Photo

Insert 3x5 Photo

Bucket List Item: _____ #_____

Date: _____   **Where:** _____

Others Present: _____

The Proof

Insert 3x5 Photo

The Moment

_____
_____
_____
_____
_____
_____
_____
_____
_____
_____
_____
_____
_____

The Facts

Why was achieving this item important to you? _____

_____

_____

What obstacles did you have to overcome to accomplish this item?

_____

_____

_____

How did your success make you feel? _____

_____

_____

RATE IT

☐ 5 Stars: Changed my life
☐ 4 Stars: Amazing
☐ 3 Stars: I'd do it again
☐ 2 Stars: Once was enough
☐ 1 Star : Not what I expected

Insert 2x2 Photo

Insert 3x5 Photo

Bucket List Item: _____ #____

Date: _____ **Where:** _____

Others Present: _____

The Proof

Insert 3x5 Photo

The Moment

_____
_____
_____
_____
_____
_____
_____
_____
_____
_____
_____
_____
_____
_____

Why was achieving this item important to you? _____

_____

_____

What obstacles did you have to overcome to accomplish this item?

_____

_____

_____

How did your success make you feel? _____

_____

_____

RATE IT

❑ 5 Stars: Changed my life
❑ 4 Stars: Amazing
❑ 3 Stars: I'd do it again
❑ 2 Stars: Once was enough
❑ 1 Star : Not what I expected

Insert 2x2 Photo

Insert 3x5 Photo

Bucket List Item: _____ #_____

Date: _____ **Where:** _____

Others Present: _____

The Proof

Insert 3x5 Photo

The Moment

_____
_____
_____
_____
_____
_____
_____
_____
_____
_____
_____
_____
_____
_____

The Facts

Why was achieving this item important to you? _____

_____

_____

What obstacles did you have to overcome to accomplish this item?

_____

_____

_____

How did your success make you feel? _____

_____

_____

RATE IT

❏ 5 Stars: Changed my life
❏ 4 Stars: Amazing
❏ 3 Stars: I'd do it again
❏ 2 Stars: Once was enough
❏ 1 Star : Not what I expected

Insert 2x2 Photo

Insert 3x5 Photo

Bucket List Item: _____ #____

Date: _____ **Where:** _____

Others Present: _____

The Proof

Insert 3x5 Photo

The Moment

_____
_____
_____
_____
_____
_____
_____
_____
_____
_____
_____
_____
_____
_____

The Facts

Why was achieving this item important to you? _____

_____

_____

What obstacles did you have to overcome to accomplish this item?

_____

_____

_____

How did your success make you feel? _____

_____

_____

RATE IT

❑ 5 Stars: Changed my life
❑ 4 Stars: Amazing
❑ 3 Stars: I'd do it again
❑ 2 Stars: Once was enough
❑ 1 Star : Not what I expected

Insert 2x2 Photo

Insert 3x5 Photo

Bucket List Item: _____ #____

Date: _____ **Where:** _____

Others Present: _____

The Proof

Insert 3x5 Photo

The Moment

_____

_____

_____

_____

_____

_____

_____

_____

_____

_____

_____

_____

_____

_____

The Facts

Why was achieving this item important to you? _____

_____

_____

What obstacles did you have to overcome to accomplish this item?

_____

_____

_____

How did your success make you feel? _____

_____

_____

RATE IT

❑ 5 Stars: Changed my life
❑ 4 Stars: Amazing
❑ 3 Stars: I'd do it again
❑ 2 Stars: Once was enough
❑ 1 Star : Not what I expected

Insert 2x2 Photo

Insert 3x5 Photo

Bucket List Item: _____ #____

Date: _____   **Where:** _____

Others Present: _____

The Proof

Insert 3x5 Photo

The Moment

_____
_____
_____
_____
_____
_____
_____
_____
_____
_____
_____
_____
_____

The Facts

Why was achieving this item important to you? _____

_____

_____

What obstacles did you have to overcome to accomplish this item?

_____

_____

_____

How did your success make you feel? _____

_____

_____

RATE IT

❑ 5 Stars: Changed my life
❑ 4 Stars: Amazing
❑ 3 Stars: I'd do it again
❑ 2 Stars: Once was enough
❑ 1 Star : Not what I expected

Insert 2x2 Photo

Insert 3x5 Photo

Bucket List Item: _____ #_____

Date: _____ **Where:** _____

Others Present: _____

The Proof

Insert 3x5 Photo

The Moment

_____
_____
_____
_____
_____
_____
_____
_____
_____
_____
_____
_____
_____

The Facts

Why was achieving this item important to you? _____
_____
_____

What obstacles did you have to overcome to accomplish this item?
_____
_____
_____

How did your success make you feel? _____
_____
_____

RATE IT

❑ 5 Stars: Changed my life
❑ 4 Stars: Amazing
❑ 3 Stars: I'd do it again
❑ 2 Stars: Once was enough
❑ 1 Star : Not what I expected

Insert 2x2 Photo

Insert 3x5 Photo

Bucket List Item: _____ #____

Date: _____ **Where:** _____

Others Present: _____

Insert 3x5 Photo

The Moment

_____
_____
_____
_____
_____
_____
_____
_____
_____
_____
_____
_____
_____

The Facts

Why was achieving this item important to you? _____

_____

_____

What obstacles did you have to overcome to accomplish this item?

_____

_____

_____

How did your success make you feel? _____

_____

_____

RATE IT

❑ 5 Stars: Changed my life
❑ 4 Stars: Amazing
❑ 3 Stars: I'd do it again
❑ 2 Stars: Once was enough
❑ 1 Star : Not what I expected

Insert 2x2 Photo

Insert 3x5 Photo

Bucket List Item: _____ #_____

Date: _____ **Where:** _____

Others Present: _____

The Proof

Insert 3x5 Photo

The Moment

_____
_____
_____
_____
_____
_____
_____
_____
_____
_____
_____
_____
_____
_____

The Facts

Why was achieving this item important to you? _____
_____
_____

What obstacles did you have to overcome to accomplish this item?
_____
_____
_____

How did your success make you feel? _____
_____
_____

RATE IT

❑ 5 Stars: Changed my life
❑ 4 Stars: Amazing
❑ 3 Stars: I'd do it again
❑ 2 Stars: Once was enough
❑ 1 Star : Not what I expected

Insert 2x2 Photo

Insert 3x5 Photo

ACCOMPLISHMENTS

Congratulations! You have achieved fifty goals that hopefully have enriched and deepened your life in some measure. Take a moment and look back at all you've done and celebrate. Then, when you're ready, write some thoughts about your accomplishments.

What bucket list item are you most proud of achieving and why?

_____
_____
_____

What bucket list item was the most difficult to achieve and why?

_____
_____
_____

What bucket list item was the easiest to achieve and why?

_____
_____
_____

What bucket list item would you recommend to others and why?

_____
_____
_____

What bucket list item would you never do again and why?

_____
_____
_____

I don't want to get to the end of my life and find that I lived just the length of it. I want to have lived the width of it as well. ~ Judith Ackerman

THOUGHTS ON MY ACHIEVEMENTS

OPEN BOOK MEDIA, LLC.

Open Book Media, LLC publishes The Bucket List, Annual Memory Book, Meditations & Affirmations, and other specialty journals and books. To learn more, and sign up for updates on future releases (including new annual editions), visit
https://www.openbookmediallc.com or
https://www.journals-for-life.com

Made in the USA
Las Vegas, NV
10 April 2022

47195475R00069